和月伸宏

NOBUHIRO WATSUKI

NAME DIVINATION

BEFORE I WAS PUBLISHED, I HAD A FRIEND
OF MINE DO A "READING" ON MY NAME.
BOTH MY REAL NAME AND MY PEN NAME
CAME OUT TO THE EFFECT, "WILL ACHIEVE A
PORTION OF SUCCESS, BUT WILL ALSO BE
FOREVER LONELY." THESE DAYS, I'VE
BEGUN TO THINK THEY WEREN'T TOO FAR
FROM THE MARK. AS WATSUKI HAS NEVER
PLACED THAT HIGH A PREMIUM ON HIS PER-
SONAL RELATIONSHIPS (BLAMING THE BUSI-
NESS), PERHAPS HE'S BROUGHT IT UPON
HIMSELF. STILL, I'M GOING TO DO WHAT I
CAN, MEANING THAT I'LL KEEP NEEDING
YOUR SUPPORT, NOW MORE THAN EVER....

Rurouni Kenshin, which has found
fans not only in Japan but around
the world, first made its appearance
in 1992, as an original short story in
Weekly Shonen Jump Special. Later
rewritten and published as a regular,
continuing *Jump* series in 1994,
Rurouni Kenshin ended serialization
in 1999 but continued in popularity,
as evidenced by the 2000 publica-
tion of *Yahiko no Sakabatô*
("Yahiko's Reversed-Edge Sword")
in *Weekly Shonen Jump*. His most
current work, *Busô Renkin*
("Armored Alchemist"), began pub-
lication in June 2003, also in *Jump*.

RUROUNI KENSHIN
VOL. 12: THE GREAT KYOTO FIRE
The SHONEN JUMP Graphic Novel Edition

STORY AND ART BY
NOBUHIRO WATSUKI

English Adaptation/Gerard Jones
Translation/Kenichiro Yagi
Touch-Up Art & Lettering/Steve Dutro
Cover, Graphics & Layout/Sean Lee
Editor/Avery Gotoh

Supervising Editor/Kit Fox
Managing Editor/Elizabeth Kawasaki
Director of Production/Noboru Watanabe
Editorial Director/Alvin Lu
Executive Vice President & Editor in Chief/Hyoe Narita
Sr. Director of Acquisitions/Rika Inouye
Vice President of Sales & Marketing/Liza Coppola
Vice President of Strategic Development/Yumi Hoashi
Publisher/Seiji Horibuchi

Printed in the U.S.A.

Published by VIZ, LLC
P.O. Box 77010
San Francisco, CA 94107

SHONEN JUMP Graphic Novel Edition
10 9 8 7 6 5 4 3 2 1
First printing, February 2005

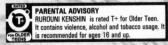

PARENTAL ADVISORY
RUROUNI KENSHIN is rated T+ for Older Teen.
It contains violence, alcohol and tobacco usage. It
is recommended for ages 16 and up.

THE WORLD'S
MOST POPULAR MANGA

www.viz.com

www.shonenjump.com

STORY AND ART BY
NOBUHIRO WATSUKI

MEIJI SWORDSMAN ROMANTIC STORY
Vol. 12: THE GREAT KYOTO FIRE

Once he was *hitokiri*, an assassin, called Battōsai. His name was legend among the *Ishin Shishi* pro-Imperialist or "patriot" warriors who launched the Meiji Era. Now, Himura Kenshin is *rurouni*, a wanderer, and carries a reversed-edge *sakabatō* to prohibit himself from killing.

Ōkubo Toshimichi, head of the government's "Internal Affairs," tries to hire Kenshin to assassinate Shishio Makoto, the successor to "Hitokiri Battōsai." But it is Ōkubo who is assassinated, and Kenshin sets out for Kyoto to find his killers. On the East Sea Road, Kenshin meets a girl named Misao and travels with her to a village occupied by Shishio's men—where he reconnects with fellow swordsman Saitō Hajime. There, they encounter Shishio himself, but the assassin refuses to fight Kenshin (because he is no longer *hitokiri*) and vanishes. Instead, Kenshin fights Sōjirō... shattering his *sakabatō*.

THUS FAR

In Kyoto, Kenshin stays at Aoi-Ya—an inn run by Okina, Misao's ex-Oniwabanshū surrogate father—and, to save Seikū (son of late swordsmith Arai Shakkū) and his family, is forced to battle Chō, a *Juppongatana* or "Ten Swords" assassin. Having been given the new *sakabatō* "Shinuchi," Kenshin goes to see Hiko Seijūrō, current master of his school of swordsmanship. But Seijūrō refuses to teach Kenshin the ultimate Hiten Mitsurugi move, saying, "One who sides with any powers or parties does not deserve the secret." Just then, Misao leads in Yahiko and Kaoru... and Seijūrō, having been convinced by Kaoru that Kenshin *has* internalized the principles of Hiten Mitsurugi on his own, decides that he will teach him the secret.

Meanwhile, Shinomori Aoshi—spurned by Okina as a prospective spy—decides to take his information on Kenshin to Shishio. Okina tries to stop him, but Aoshi has rid himself of compassion and has turned into a kind of demon. With Okina's death, Misao proclaims herself *Okashira* or "head" of the Oniwabanshū, swearing to defeat Shishio and his men... including her beloved Aoshi-sama. Elsewhere, at the police department, Sanosuke has contacted Saitō and together the two interrogate Chō, learning that Shishio is about to launch his grand scheme, which begins with the burning of Kyoto....

CONTENTS

RUROUNI KENSHIN
Meiji Swordsman Romantic Story
BOOK TWELVE: THE GREAT KYOTO FIRE

WH...
WHAT...

...ARE
YOU?!

YOU WERE UNLUCKY, CHILD. THE SHŌGUNATE'S LAWS HAVE BEEN LAX SINCE THE ARRIVAL OF THE BLACK SHIPS TWO YEARS AGO. MORE AND MORE SELF-DECLARED RŌNIN PROWL AS BANDITS IN THIS AREA.

SOME FATE BROUGHT ME HERE, AND I HAVE TAKEN REVENGE FOR YOU.

BUT THE DEAD WILL NOT BE BROUGHT BACK TO LIFE BY MOURNING OR HATRED.

10

...WELL, IF YOU WON'T GET UP...

...I'LL CONTINUE MY STROLL DOWN MEMORY LANE.

HH HH HH

VA—

KLUP

LET'S SEE, THE LAST TIME YOU WET YOUR BED WAS WHEN YOU WERE 11 YEARS OLD...

KOOP!

IT'S NOT FAIR.

IT'S TAKEN YEARS TO FORGET THOSE THINGS!

...THEN THERE WAS THE TIME YOU ATE "LAUGHING MUSHROOM" AND NEARLY GUFFAWED YOURSELF TO DEATH...

I'M TOO SELFLESS FOR MY OWN GOOD.

NO? AND IT IS FAIR FOR ME TO SPEND A WHOLE WEEK RETRAINING THE IDIOT APPRENTICE WHO RAN OUT ON ME?

MASTER!

13

飛天

ひてん

HITEN...

御剣流

み つるぎ りゅう

...MITSURUGI-
RYU...

GASP

...SO YOU FORGOT ABOUT YOUR LANDING, AND WHACKED YOUR HEAD. IDIOT.

YOU FOCUSED ALL YOUR CONCENTRATION ONLY ON YOUR SWING...

I WOULDN'T CALL IT PERFECT... ...BUT A STRIKE IS A STRIKE.

...YOU COULDN'T HAVE LANDED A BLOW ON ME IN TEN YEARS.

BUT IF YOU HADN'T DONE THAT...

ZIP

19

I'LL START YOUR INITIATION INTO THE SECRET.

NOW, DON'T MOVE EVEN A HAIR.

IF YOU DO, YOU'LL DIE. SIMPLE AS THAT.

THESE ARE THE SWORD-STRIKES.

LISTEN WELL.

20

THIS IS THE HITEN MITSURUGI-RYŪ...

...KUZU-RYŪSEN—"NINE-HEADED DRAGON."

NOT A FINGER COULD BE MOVED...

THIS IS THE SECRET!

AND, AS A CHARGING ATTACK, IT'S ALSO IMPOSSIBLE TO DODGE.

UNLIKE ANOTHER MULTIPLE STRIKE, "DRAGON'S LAIR" RYŪSŌSEN, ALL NINE STRIKES OF KUZU-RYŪSEN CARRY FATAL IMPACT.

GLINT

OF ALL MY MOVES, IT IS THE GREATEST.

Act 95
Even If It
Costs My Life

HITEN MITSURUGI-RYŪ, "KUZU-RYŪSEN."

...THE *SECRET* OF HITEN MITSURUGI-RYŪ!

A CHARGE AND NINE STRIKES, IMPOSSIBLE TO DEFEND OR DODGE...

HEH

YOU LEARN BY *OVERREACHING* YOURSELF, BY GETTING YOURSELF *WHACKED*.

YOU DON'T LEARN MOVES STEP BY STEP.

IT'S HOW YOU'VE *ALWAYS* TRAINED.

★

QUIT BABBLING.

WHAT...?! I-I CAN'T JUST...

STOP GAPING AND DO IT.

RYŪTSUISEN

RYŪSHŌSEN

龍槌閃

龍翔閃

龍巻閃

RYŪKANSEN

HE'S RIGHT...

IT HELPS THAT I'VE ALWAYS ADJUSTED THE FORCE.

WELL...

IT'S A WONDER THEY WEREN'T FATAL...

Long time no see! Watsuki here. Since here is the only space we've got this time, let's get the usual nonsense out of the way:

• "Samurai Spirits: Zankurō Musōken"...my friend showed me it. I'm totally into "rasetsu—mode" Genjūrō!! Throwing—weapons ricocheting...triple spins in mid—air! I'm crazy about "Samu-Supi." I can't get enough.

• I read the American comic, "Silver Surfer." I never thought it was for me, but it turns out it's a really deep story!! The Surfer is so classy...and so lonely. Everyone at work's passed it around. Give it a try if you have the chance.

• The "Spawn" toys from the American comic series are so far out there, they're great... especially the 13—inch figure. That one's so cool. I keep it on my desk, rather than on the display shelf. I hope McFarlane Toys can keep it up. Hurray for the toy biz!

• A serious topic for a change. My personal relationships lately have been pretty unstable. Usually, the problem's with me, but sometimes it's the other person, and that depresses me. I've started thinking about responsibility—it's hard to explain what I'm getting at, but I think about AIDS being spread by medication, or a cult like Aum [Shinri-kyō]. People don't take responsibility for what they do. I can't fix other people, but as an individual, I'm trying to be as aware as I can.

• My replies to your fan letters have ground to a complete halt. I'm so sorry about that. I am reading them, at least, so I hope you'll hang in there with me (and here I was just going on about responsibility, too).

See you next volume!

MULTIPLE STRIKES DEPEND ON ARM STRENGTH. CHARGES DEPEND ON WEIGHT.

IN BOTH AREAS, YOU'RE INFERIOR.

BUT EVEN WHEN THE MOVE IS *EXACTLY* THE SAME...

...IF THE WIELDER IS DIFFERENT, THE *FORCE* WILL BE DIFFERENT.

...YOUR "NINE HEADS" ARE NOTHING.

SO, WHEN YOU FACE MY KUZU-RYŪSEN...

BUT THERE *IS* ONE MOVE THAT CAN DEFEAT MINE...

...AND *ONLY* ONE.

AH.

THEN...

...THE KUZU-RYŪSEN CAN NEVER...!

KUZU-RYŪSEN WASN'T CREATED FOR BATTLE, BUT AS A *TEST* FOR THE INITIATION INTO THE SECRET.

THE INITIATE TRADITIONALLY FACES IT FIRST...

THINK *HARD* ABOUT THE NATURE OF KUZU-RYŪSEN.

THE "AMAKAKERU RYU NO HIRAMEKI" WILL APPEAR.

BUT...

...HE WILL BE CONSIDERED *READY* FOR THE SECRET.

...AND, IF HE CAN OVERCOME HIS *MASTER'S* NINE DRAGONS...

THE *NATURE* OF KUZU-RYŪSEN...

37

HYAAAH

SHK

KEEN

TO DEFEAT IT...IT MUST BE COUNTERED WITH BATTŌJUTSU, BEFORE IT'S DELIVERED.

...IS THAT OF A MOVE THAT CAN'T BE BLOCKED OR DODGED.

THAT IS THE TRUE SECRET OF THE DRAGON FLIGHT OF HEAVEN.

AS FAST AS IT IS, YOUR BATTŌJUTSU MUST BE FASTER STILL.

...VERY GOOD.

EXACTLY RIGHT.

RECKLESS.

"BACK TO THE RIVER," IS IT THEN?*

MAYBE SO.

*TO GIVE EVERYTHING YOU HAVE, AWARE THERE'S NO CHANCE OF RECOVERY IF YOU FAIL.

I MUST TRY FOR THE SECRET... EVEN IF IT COSTS MY LIFE.

BUT THERE'S NO CHOICE.

...

WHAT?

YOU ARE MY IDIOT PUPIL.

MASTER...

WHEN IT COMES DOWN TO IT, YOU DON'T UNDER- STAND A THING.

TP

I GIVE YOU ONE NIGHT.

SEARCH YOUR SOUL AND FIND WHAT'S LACKING IN YOU BEFORE SUNRISE.

SS

IF YOU CANNOT DO THAT, YOU WILL NOT ONLY FAIL TO OBTAIN THE SECRET...

...BUT HERE WILL ALSO BE WHERE YOU LOSE YOUR LIFE.

●●●

42

43

...SPRING FROM THE CORPSE OF A JAPAN DECOMPOSING.

I KILL AND KILL, AND STILL THE VILLAINS, LIKE MAGGOTS...

...TOO MANY TIMES, I CANNOT SAVE A SOUL.

EVEN WHEN I WIELD MY SWORD ACCORDING TO THE TEACHINGS OF HITEN MITSURUGI-RYU...

AND ALL I CAN DO IS BURY THE VICTIMS.

THERE WILL BE MORE AND MORE ACTS LIKE THIS.

THEY WERE SLAVERS, NOT PARENTS.

NOT ONLY YOUR PARENTS ...

TP

TP

...DIED OF CHOLERA LAST YEAR.

THE PARENTS ...

...BUT FOR THE BANDITS, TOO.

BANDITS OR SLAVERS, ONCE THEY'RE DEAD, THEY'RE JUST BODIES.

WHAT ARE THOSE THREE STONE GRAVES?

STILL, YOU MADE GRAVES FOR THEM.

ALL THREE FORCIBLY TAKEN FROM THEIR PARENTS AS PAYMENT FOR DEBTS.

KASUMI-SAN, AKANE-SAN, SAKURA-SAN.

SO I THOUGHT, EVEN IF IT COSTS MY LIFE...

I ONLY KNEW THEM FOR A DAY, BUT I WAS THE ONLY ONE HERE, AND I HAVE NO PARENTS.

...I'LL HAVE TO PROTECT THEM.

I LOOKED FOR FLOWERS TO OFFER, BUT I COULDN'T FIND EVEN ONE.

...I COULDN'T FIND THE RIGHT STONES TO MAKE A NICE GRAVE FOR THEM, LIKE I WANTED.

BUT...

A GOOD SAKE IS THE LEAST I CAN DO.

KPOK

TUK

TUK

MAN OR WOMAN, TO ATTAIN BUDDHAHOOD WITHOUT KNOWING THE TASTE OF GOOD SAKE IS A CRIME.

48

FROM NOW ON, YOUR NAME IS TO BE "KENSHIN."

OR "SWORD-ARTS," THAT'S FAR TOO GENTLE.

WHAT IS YOUR NAME, BOY?

SHINTA.

...MY MOST PRECIOUS KNOWLEDGE.

I SHALL ALSO GIVE YOU...

"EVEN SO..."

"NINETEEN YEARS AGO."

...TOMORROW WILL SEE THE *END* OF THAT LIFE.

...WHETHER THE INITIATION IS SUCCESSFUL OR NOT...

...

Act 96
Between Life and Death

THAT'S DANGEROUS, DAYDREAMING BY THE WINDOW.

YOU NEVER KNOW WHEN THE ENEMY WILL TARGET YOU.

MISAO-CHAN...

...

NOT MISAO... OKASHIRA!

NO, NO!

TSK TSK

...HIMURA COMES BACK SOON WITH THIS "SECRET."

I HOPE...

51

...EVEN IF HE DOES GET STRONGER.

YES... BUT...

...EVEN IF HE DOES BECOME A BETTER SWORDSMAN...

OH, NO. NO, NO.

I'M SORRY. YOU'VE YOUR OWN WORRIES.

WHEN I THINK OF...

...AND EVEN IF THE FIGHT AGAINST SHISHIO IS EASIER WITH THIS POWERFUL SECRET...

...THE REAL BATTLE WILL BE INSIDE *HIM*, BETWEEN THE SOUL OF A HITOKIRI AND HIS VOW NOT TO KILL.

ME, AT LEAST, YOU DON'T...

...THAT...

...HAVE TO WORRY ABOUT.

Act 96
Between Life and Death

TWEE
TWEE
TWEE

...YOU EITHER.

YOU DIDN'T SLEEP LAST NIGHT.

DWANG

GLOOM

54

SCRIB

SCRIB SCRIB

SCRIB

...

THAT SO.

ZK

ZK

SO...

...DID YOU DISCOVER WHAT YOU WERE LACKING?

...

...NO.

...ARE A MAN WHO'S HIT HIS LIMIT.

IN THAT CASE, YOU...

ZUDDD

FWAH

ALONG WITH THE NAME "HIKO SEIJŪRŌ," THIS WHITE CLOAK, TOO, IS PASSED DOWN.

...ITS SHOULDERS ARE RIGGED WITH SPRINGS WHICH APPLY COUNTER-PRESSURE IN THE AMOUNT OF TEN KAN*.

*TEN KAN=37.5 KG.

TO RESTRAIN IN TIMES OF PEACE THE POWER OF THE HITEN MITSURUGI INHERITOR...

ZK

FINALLY...

...HE'S HERE.

...KENSHIN?

ARE YOU READY...

NO FEAR.

GNG

SINCE LIVING THROUGH THE CHAOS OF THE BAKUMATSU, I'VE BEEN PREPARED FOR IT.

...MY LIFE.

I *MUST* HAVE THE SECRET, EVEN IF IT COSTS...

FOR BEHIND HIM, TRULY, IS

DEATH.

...FOR THE COMING OF THE NINE-HEADED DRAGON.

PREPARE YOURSELF...

...

DEATH

YES...
THAT'S
IT.

SHH
SHH

66

...EVEN IF YOU QUELL DANGER WITH YOUR FIERCE ANGER, SACRIFICING YOUR LIFE...

...IT IS ONLY FOR ONE SHORT MOMENT IN TIME. AND TIME GOES ON.

EVEN IF YOU PROTECT THE WEAK AND THE ONES YOU LOVE BY SACRIFICING YOURSELF WITH THE COMPASSION OF THE BUDDHA HIMSELF...

...SORROW WILL *REMAIN* IN THOSE PEOPLE. THEY WILL NEVER BE *TRULY* HAPPY.

WITH IT, YOU WILL DEFEAT NOT ONLY SHISHIO, BUT THE HITOKIRI WITHIN YOU.

REMEMBER IT, AND THE AMAKAKERU RYU NO HIRAMEKI IS YOURS.

THE WILL TO LIVE IS THE HEART OF EXISTENCE.

DO NOT FORGET THAT.

MASTER...

GLINT

MASTER
!!

I, TOO, LEARNED THAT FACT AT THE EXPENSE OF MY MASTER'S LIFE.

AMAKAKERU RYŪ NO HIRAMEKI IS THE STRONGEST MOVE OF HITEN MITSURUGI-RYŪ.

THE REST IS UP TO YOU, AS... RUROUNI.

THIS IS ALL I CAN TEACH...AS THE MASTER OF MITSURUGI.

Act 97
The Ten Swords Summoned

Act 97
The Ten
Swords
Summoned

...THE *HEART MEDICATION* MASTER MADE, BACK DURING THE TIME OF THE POISON MUSHROOMS!

IT'S HERE...

HH

HH

M A S T E R !!

IT'S TOO LATE TO GO DOWN THE MOUNTAIN AND FIND A DOCTOR.

...AND WITH HIS TOUGH-NESS... MAYBE...

IT'S A LONG SHOT, BUT WITH THIS MEDICINE ...

I'M HOME...

...THERE YOU ARE!

"WHERE"?

WHERE HAVE YOU BEEN?!

WHAT'S THE MATTER? YOU LOOK MAD.

SO I WENT OUT AND BOUGHT SOME LOCAL TREATS FOR US TO SHARE.

STAYING IN THIS *HOLE* WOULD DRIVE *ANYONE* CRAZY.

LISTEN, YOU!

WELL, I COULDN'T DECIDE WHICH ONES WERE GOOD.

YOU WERE GONE THREE DAYS FOR THAT?!

WHILE YOU WERE GONE, THAT *USUI* CAME... AND IT WAS A *DISASTER*!

···

WHAT? WHAT IS IT??

WANT ONE?

USUI-SAN. LONG TIME NO SEE.

YATSU-HASHI, EH...?

STILL... LOCAL DELICACIES ONLY?

FOR YOU TO LEAVE SHISHIO'S SIDE, IT CAN ONLY BE UNDER ORDERS.

WHAT ABOUT "THAT USUI" ...?

MY SOUL'S EYE "SHINGAN" CAN SEE THROUGH THE SOUL, WHERE THE NAKED EYES CANNOT SEE.

EVEN WITH YOUR TWISTED EMOTIONS, I CAN SEE RIGHT THROUGH YOU.

HEH

HEH...

HUH?

THE LAST THREE HAVE JUST ARRIVED.

OH, YES, I FORGOT. THE *TEN SWORDS* ARE TO GATHER IN THE GREAT HALL IMMEDIATELY.

WELL, WHATEVER IT IS YOU'RE BOTH HIDING, IT'S OF NO CONCERN.

GEH.

HEY. KAMATARI-SAN.

!

SŌ-CHAN! HEY! LONG TIME NO SEE!

UH-HUH...

GLINT

AND YUMI-SAN. SAME TO YOU.

ABSOLUTELY! I'M FOR SURE NOT LOSING TO A MAN.

IF YOU ARE A MAN.

HEH HEH

THIS TIME, WE'LL SETTLE WHO WINS SHISHIO-SAMA'S HEART FOR SURE.

ELDER SAIZUCHI.

NYEH HEH HEH

NYEH-HEH-HEH-HEH. YOUTH IS SUCH A LIVELY TIME.

YOUTHS THESE DAYS, EH?

NOT ONLY WILL *THEY* NOT TALK TO ME, THEY WON'T EVEN *LOOK* AT ME.

GLAD TO SEE YOU ARE DOING WELL.

OH YEAH? AND WHERE IS YOUR PARTNER?

WHO, FUJI? HE'S OUTSIDE...

THEY'RE ALL JUST JEALOUS OF MY POWERS.

TL'H

HEH. YOU'RE THE ONLY ONE WHO SAYS SO.

...AS HE CAN'T EVEN *FIT* INTO THIS LAIR.

THAT'S ALL OF US.

ALL RIGHT.

TIP

SŌJIRŌ, WE'RE IN THE MIDDLE OF SOME-THING. LATER?

THIS IS A SOUVENIR.

IT'S GO-O-OD...

PiTCH

FORGIVE ME, SHISHIO-SAN, FOR DIS-APPEARING THESE PAST THREE DAYS.

THE PREPARATION OF THE SHIP IS COMPLETE. WE CAN SAIL ANYTIME. USUI-SAN MAY HAVE SENSED SOMETHING, BUT I WOULDN'T WORRY.

船の準備
完了しました
いつでも
出航可能です
※宇水さんが少し
勘付いたようですが
多分大丈夫でしょう

MM.

HEH.

I'LL HAVE SOME LATER.

THANK YOU FOR YOUR TROUBLE.

THANK YOU ALL FOR COMING SO FAR.

I KNOW...

...THAT I'VE MADE YOU ALL WAIT QUITE LONG.

...BUT THE REST OF US *ARE* HERE.

"SWORD HUNTER" CHŌ.

WE STILL ARE MISSING CHŌ, DUE TO AN UNEXPECTED INCIDENT...

...WE WILL MAKE THE GREAT KYOTO FIRE A REALITY.

TOMORROW, JUST BEFORE MIDNIGHT...

AND SO...

...THE SUN ROSE ON THE DAY OF DESTINY.

CHEE
CHEE
CHEE

BOOT!!

WHAT ARE YOU LYING AROUND SNOOZING FOR?!

LOOK HERE. THE STAY PIN HAS COME OUT TO THE POINT WHERE THE BLADE'S ALMOST LOOSE ENOUGH TO COME OUT.

SAKABATŌ SHINUCHI!

SS

IF I HAD TO GUESS...

...IT'D BE THIS SWORD.

THE POWER OF AMAKAKERU RYŪ NO HIRAMEKI WAS ABSORBED BY THE BLADE JUST ENOUGH TO WEAKEN IT.

...THAT CONSIDERS ITS WIELDER'S FEELINGS.

IT IS A GREAT SWORD INDEED...

SHAKKŪ-DONO...

OF COURSE, IT WAS MY PERFECT TRAINING THAT MADE IT POSSIBLE FOR ME TO STRIKE YOUR SWORD AT THAT EXACT POINT.

GLINT

...

FROM HERE ON, AS RUROUNI...

...TRAIN TO ADJUST YOUR STRENGTH TO A MORE PRECISE LEVEL WITH YOUR WILL.

AS YOU CAN SEE, IT GIVES EVEN A SAKABATO ENOUGH POWER TO KILL.

WHAP

IN ANY CASE, YOUR INITIATION INTO THE SECRET IS NOW COMPLETE.

HYOO

...

YES.

...

GOOD.

...AND *GET BACK* TO THE PEOPLE WAITING FOR YOU.

NOW, QUIT WASTING TIME, *LEAVE* THE MOUNTAIN...

The Secret Life of Characters (32)
—Hiko Seijūrō—

Personality-wise, there's no model. When Watsuki sat down to imagine what sort of guy the "Master" might be, the character at first became this arrogant, twisted guy. As one of my favorites, I actually wanted to give the guy more appearances...but then again, he *is* stronger than Kenshin and, as my editor puts it, "(The Master) is like the joker in a card deck." In other words, he's just too powerful—it's hard to find a place to use him.

This is a little off-topic, but lately Watsuki has found himself fascinated by images of "manliness," and Hiko is one of the first characters to reflect that fascination. The drinking scenes come from Watsuki's own low tolerance for alcohol, and because Watsuki sees a sort of manliness in the image of a man drinking alone (not that Hiko is a drunk). There've been lots of questions lately asking if this Hiko is related to the Hiko Seijūrō in "Crescent Moon of the Warring States," but as Hiten Mitsurugi-ryū is passed on through potential, and not blood, there's no *biological* relation, no.

The Hiko Seijūrō of "Crescent Moon" is the model design-wise (of course), but I also threw in a bit of "Hiken Majin Hamerun" from Master Obata's "Arabian Lamp Lamp" (Obata-*shishō*, forgive me!).

In setting the character within the context of "RuroKen," I ended up simplifying his design, such as fixing his hair to be easier to draw. What with his being a completely different type of Hiten Mitsurugi-ryū swordsman, and with the above-mentioned "manliness" as well, his body became a macho one. If there are female fans who liked the face but not so much the body, sorry about that! (Still, if every new character was "just another good-looking guy," how interesting would that be? Watsuki knows *he* wouldn't enjoy it....)

As for the cloak...okay, yes...there's a bit of the American comic "Spawn" in it.

THANK YOU FOR EVERYTHING.

WELL, MASTER...

HOLD ON.

YOU'VE EARNED IT.

TAKE IT.

THE WHITE CLOAK PASSED DOWN TO EACH NEW GENERATION... ...IS LIKE A SYMBOL FOR THE INHERITOR OF HITEN MITSURUGI-RYŪ.

Act 98—The Other Objective

IMAGINED...

予想図

...RESULT

完成

...

...

LOOOOM

I MUST DECLINE.

EX- CUSE ME!!

LOOKS AWFUL ON ME ANYWAY.

...ARE HITEN MITSURUGI- RYŪ TEACHINGS.

ALL I INTEND TO KEEP...

...OR OF CARRYING ON HITEN MITSURUGI- RYŪ.

I'M SORRY. MASTER, BUT I'VE NO INTENTION OF BECOMING THE 14TH "HIKO SEIJŪRŌ"...

SELFISH AS EVER, I SEE.

94

WHILE I FIGHT AGAINST SHISHIO'S MEN, WILL YOU PROTECT...

SELFISH OR NOT...

...I'VE ONE MORE REQUEST.

WELL...

...MY FRIENDS AT AOI-YA?

...I DON'T SUPPOSE I SHOULD BE SURPRISED.

...

JAB

MASTER?

HUH.

TIME FOR YOU TO GROW UP, DAMMIT!

VHIP

FROM THE MOMENT YOU SAID YOU WOULDN'T CARRY ON HITEN MITSURUGI-RYŪ...

...YOU AND I CEASED TO BE MASTER AND APPRENTICE.

WASH

STILL... I DID NOT TEACH YOU THE SECRET TO MAKE YOU *SUFFER*.

REMEMBER THAT.

MASTER!

FORGET THAT I WAS EVER YOUR MASTER.

DON'T WORRY ABOUT YOUR FRIENDS.

JUST GO SETTLE WITH SHISHIO.

BOW

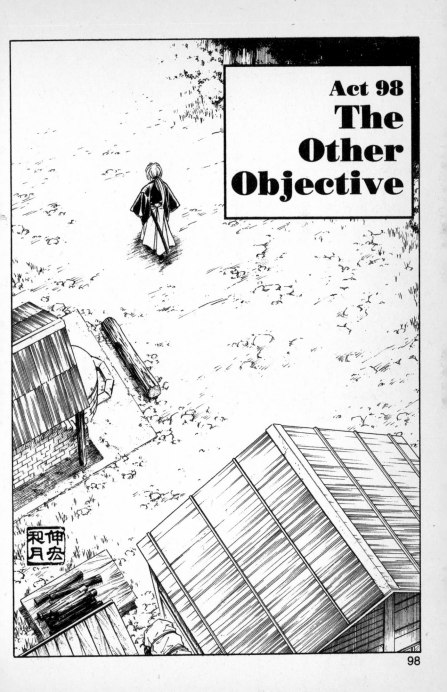

Act 98
The Other Objective

BLAH

BLAH

YADA

YADA

A LOT OF POLICE OUT TODAY, TOO...

DID SOMETHING HAPPEN?

EVERY-BODY'S SO WORKED UP.

YADA YADA

...

...BE SO SURE.

I WOULDN'T...

STUBB

WITH REINFORCEMENTS FROM OTHER PREFECTURES, WE'LL HAVE NEARLY 5,000 MEN BY EVENING. EVEN *SHISHIO* WON'T BE ABLE TO RUN WILD THEN.

I'VE REASSIGNED AS MANY MEN AS I CAN TO KYOTO PATROL... PER YOUR REQUEST, FUJITA-KUN.

DON'T WORRY. IT'LL BE FINE.

HEAVEN'S ON OUR SIDE, IT SEEMS.

HUH?

THANKS.

100

THAT... LEGENDARY MAN WE WERE SEARCHING FOR...APPEARED AT AMAGATAKE STATION THIS MORNING.

I TOLD HIM TO COME BY CARRIAGE, RIGHT AWAY.

KLATTA KLATTA

HE SHOULD BE HERE ANY MINUTE.

KLATTA KLATTA

SKRK

KCH...

...SPEAK OF THE DEVIL.

WELL.

THAT... IS THE HITOKIRI...

...HIMURA BATTŌSAI.

PLAYING "RICH MAN," ARE YOU?

RIDING UP IN A CARRIAGE ON A WEEKDAY AFTER-NOON.

102

...SET FIRE TO KYOTO?!

SO SAYS YOUR CAPTIVE, CHŌ OF THE TEN SWORDS.

MM.

THE "GREAT KYOTO FIRE" IS TO BE SPARKED TONIGHT AT 11:59.

THAT SEEMS CERTAIN.

HE CONFESSED TO BEING ONE OF SHISHIO'S MEN, GETTING READY FOR TONIGHT'S FIRE.

THEN, THIS MORNING, WE PICKED UP A SUSPICIOUS CHARACTER FOR INTERROGATION.

...SOMETHING'S ODD.

YOU THINK SO, TOO?

ARSON FITS THAT STRATEGY PERFECTLY.

WE OUTNUMBER SHISHIO'S FORCES OVERWHELMINGLY, SO HIS STRATEGY HAS TO BE SURPRISE ATTACKS AND ASSASSINATIONS.

NO LONGER WILL WE HIDE IN THIS CAVE!

MEN! THE TIME HAS COME!

NOW WE UNVEIL OUR POWERS TO THE DECADENT AGE!

BUT IF THEIR INFORMATION IS LEAKED THIS EASILY, THEY'D HAVE NO CHANCE AT A SURPRISE.

HSH

SO I'VE BEEN WAITING FOR ONE OF THE JUPPONGATANA TO COME HERE AND ASSASSINATE THEIR COMRADE, CHŌ.

SECRECY IS A MATTER OF LIFE AND DEATH TO THEM.

IT'S AS IF THEY *WANTED* US TO GET THAT INFORMATION.

...WE STRIKE!

NOW...

BUT IT HASN'T HAPPENED.

RAAAAAAAAAAAAAAAAH!

...THERE'S SOMETHING BEHIND THE KYOTO FIRE THAT EVEN THE *TEN SWORDS* HAVEN'T BEEN TOLD.

PER-HAPS...

...SOME-THING IS OFF.

IN ANY CASE...

106

...OTHER OBJECTIVE.

PERHAPS SOME...

THEY'RE MODELING THEIR FIRE AFTER THE IKEDA-YA INCIDENT.

SHISHIO HAS A DRAMATIC STREAK. THE "OTHER OBJECTIVE" *MUST* HAVE A SIMILAR QUALITY OF "PLAY" TO IT.

...WAIT.

BUT WHAT?

WHAT IS THEIR...?

FWAAAP!

IF SHISHIO IS TRYING TO MAKE SOME IRONIC *COMMENTARY*, THEN THE *REAL* TARGET OF HIS ATTACK...

...SHŌGUN TOKUGAWA YOSHINOBU DECEIVED HIS OWN MEN, AND SAILED FOR EDO FROM OSAKA BAY. *THAT* WAS THE MAIN REASON FOR THE IMPERIAL ARMY'S VICTORY.

SAITŌ...AT THE TURNING POINT OF THE BAKUMATSU, DURING THE BOSHIN WAR AND THE BATTLE OF TOBA-FUSHIMI...

THE KYOTO FIRE IS ONLY A *DIVERSION!* HIS *TRUE* OBJECTIVE IS TO FIRE AT TOKYO FROM THE SEA!

TOKYO (EDO)

...IS HERE!

THAT'S WHY HE LEAKED INFORMATION TO US!

YES...IF HE CAN LURE ENOUGH MANPOWER HERE...

...DRAW EVERYONE'S ATTENTION WITH A BATTLE BETWEEN HIS MEN AND THE POLICE...

108

Act 99
As If in Flight

113

SAITŌ, WHAT ARE YOU DOING?!

WITH YOU YELLING, WE CAN'T TALK.

SHUT IT AWHILE, HUH?

TO CONTINUE...

5,000 POLICEMEN HAVE BEEN ASSIGNED TO KYOTO.

WE OUTNUMBER SHISHIO TEN TIMES.

WITH THAT FORCE, WE SHOULD AT LEAST BE ABLE TO STOP THE FIRE.

THE POLICE CAN STOP 500 SOLDIERS, BUT NOT 500 SPARKS.

BUT WHAT WAS IT?

DON'T WORRY. I'M HAVING IT DELIVERED.

THAT LETTER BEFORE WE LEFT...

115

BUT...

HEY. MISAO-CHAN?

...IF WE'RE GOING TO FIGHT SHISHIO'S MEN, I THOUGHT MAYBE WE SHOULD HAVE SOME EXTRA POWER.

I'D RATHER NOT HAVE TO DEPEND ON FIREARMS, BUT...

IT STILL ONLY TOOK FOUR ONIWABANSHŪ TO *DEFEAT* IT.

GATLING GUNS ARE INCREDIBLY POWERFUL. PROBABLY THE MOST POWERFUL WEAPONS YOU CAN *USE* AGAINST PEOPLE.

THE TRUE STRENGTH OF THE ONIWABANSHŪ ISN'T SOMETHING YOU CAN *BUY*, IS IT?

OH, THERE THEY ARE.

...

I THINK THAT'S WHY KENSHIN RESPECTS YOU SO MUCH.

LOOK! A LETTER, A LETTER!!

A LETTER FROM KENSHIN!!

NO IDEA... BUT THIS SCRAGGLY WRITING IS DEFINITELY KENSHIN!

A POLICE-MAN? WHY?

A POLICE-MAN DELIVERED IT!

HURRY UP AND OPEN IT!

...

...

118

SETTING FIRE TO KYOTO...

...IT'S... MAD...

I WONDERED WHY SO MANY POLICE...

...IT CAN'T BE...

WHAT DO WE DO... MISAO-CHAN?

SO WHAT ELSE IS NEW WITH THEM?!

STOP IT AT ALL COSTS!!

WHAT ELSE?!

RELEASE THE CARRIER PIGEONS!

CONTACT EVERYONE IN KYOTO!

KUROJŌ, SHIROJŌ, MASU-KAMI, ŌMIME!

EVERYONE, INTO YOUR SHINOBI ROBES!

VPP

STILL... FIGHTING ALONGSIDE ONIWABANSHŪ...

IT'S THE LAST THING I WOULD'VE THOUGHT, WHEN WE FOUGHT 'EM IN TOKYO

YOU KNOW IT!

IT'S TIME FOR THE KYOTO ONIWABANSHŪ TO ACT!

120

I'VE SENT A TELEGRAM TO OSAKA...

BUT MOST OF THEIR MEN ARE IN KYOTO, SO A SIEGE IS IMPOSSIBLE.

AND THIS CARNAGE WON'T GET THERE UNTIL MIDNIGHT.

THERE'LL BE NO TIME FOR A THOROUGH SEARCH...

EVEN IF WE SCREW UP, TOKYO WON'T GO DOWN IN ONE OR TWO CANNON BLASTS.

ALL WE CAN DO NOW IS HIT THEM WITH ALL WE'VE GOT!

ALL WE CAN DO IS DO WHAT WE CAN!

!

WE HAVE NO TIME!

BE SWIFT IN YOUR ACTIONS...

...AS IF IN FLIGHT !!!

DIDN'T I TELL YOU TO *SHUT IT,* BLOCKHEAD?

WE'RE TALKING, HERE.

ONCE, YOU GET AWAY WITH!! BUT TWICE—!!

URK ?!

SANO... DESTROYING TOKYO ISN'T WHAT SHISHIO'S AFTER.

!

JA BB

IN THE 6TH YEAR OF KAEI, PERRY ARRIVED AT THE SHORE OF URAGA. THE BLACK SHIPS MARKED THE START OF THE BAKUMATSU.

SEEING THOSE MONSTERS FOR THE FIRST TIME, PEOPLE SANG, "STEAMBOATS BREAK THE SLUMBER OF THE GREAT SEA/ THO' THEY BE BUT FOUR/THERE'S NO SLEEP THIS NIGHT." THE CITY OF EDO PANICKED.

THE FEAR OF THAT MOMENT—THE CHAOS OF THE BAKUMATSU— IT'S STILL DEEP WITHIN PEOPLE'S SOULS...EVEN IF IT IS "TOKYO" NOW.

...THE CITY WILL FALL INTO PANDEMONIUM.

EVEN IF *ONE* UNKNOWN SHIP APPEARS AND STARTS FIRING AT TOKYO...

YEAH...

...

THE CURRENT GOVERNMENT WOULD HAVE NO POWER TO QUELL IT...

...AND TOKYO WOULD BECOME A LAWLESS ZONE. THE GOVERNMENT WOULD STOP FUNCTION- ING.

THE SITUATION GETS WORSE WITH EVERY HOUR.

I GET IT.

...AS IF IN FLIGHT !!

AND THAT'S WHY WE MUST HURRY...

HYAH!

OSAKA BAY

...

BUT DO WE REALLY HAVE TO GO...

I AM HONORED TO BE INCLUDED IN THE ASSAULT ON TOKYO, WHICH WAS KEPT SECRET EVEN FROM THE JUPPON-GATANA.

TROUBLED, YUMI?

...ON THIS BROKEN-DOWN BOAT?

UWA?

WAS IT MY *LOOKS* YOU FELL IN LOVE WITH?

TELL ME, YUMI.

GLIC...

...THAT TWO THINGS MAKE THE JOB OF HITOKIRI EASIER.

LIFE DURING THE BAKUMATSU TAUGHT ME...

KLATTA

...HAS ALREADY BEEN MET.

THE FIRST CONDITION, AS YOU WILL AGREE...

KLATTA KLATTA KLATTA

THE ABILITY TO BLEND INTO DARKNESS...

...WILL REQUIRE A BIT OF SHAPE-CHANGING.

THE SECOND...

...AND THE ABILITY TO BLEND INTO A CROWD.

126

IF SO, TAKE A LOOK...

...AT WHAT'S INSIDE HERE.

WHAT WOULD *SHISHIO* DO...?

SHISHIO MAKOTO TOOK THIS ONE'S PLACE AS HITOKIRI.

OR DID YOU FALL FOR WHAT'S INSIDE ME?

...KNOWS IT LIKE HIS OWN PALM.

"HITOKIRI BATTŌSAI"...

...AS A MERCHANT VESSEL...

HE'D DISGUISE HIS SHIP...

...AND *RENGOKU* SETS SAIL.

THIRTY-SEVEN MINUTES UNTIL THE FIRE BEGINS...

THIRTY-SEVEN MINUTES UNTIL...

...IT ALL COMES TOGETHER.

...IT'S TIME.

REPORT!!

WHERE ARE THE FLAMES?! THEY'RE LATE!

OR THE 2ND UNIT!

THERE ARE TOO MANY POLICE ALL OVER KYOTO! THE FIRST UNIT CAN'T ACT!

AND THE 3RD IS...

DON'T BE IMPATIENT. FIRE DOESN'T SPREAD THAT EASILY.

133

KILLING POLICE AND CITIZENS IS *NOT* OUR JOB!!

USUI, THE DUTY OF THE TEN SWORDS IS TO KILL GOVERNMENT OFFICIALS.

WE'LL CREATE A DIVERSION TO MAKE IT EASIER FOR YOU TO DO YOUR WORK.

HEH

WE'VE NO CHOICE BUT TO CHANGE OUR PLANS.

AUGH! YOU FOOLS ARE USELESS!

FEH.

THEY WILL DIE ANYWAY.

ONCE THE FLAMES SPREAD, IT'S ALL THE SAME.

OH.

DON'T BOTHER, IDIOT. YOU'LL GET IN THE WAY.

FUJI AND I WILL DECLINE.

UH... I'M IN.

...

TP.

I'LL DO IT!

LOOK, I WON'T FORCE YOU.

134

Act 100

The Great Kyoto Fire (Part I)

137

142

GOOD JOB!!

BUT IT'S ONLY JUST STARTED, SO STAY ALERT!!

HEY, MISAO-CHAN.. I MEAN, OKASHIRA!!

WE GOT 'EM DOWN HERE!

WILL DO.

YOU BE CAREFUL TOO, MISA... OKASHIRA.

NOW... EVERYONE GO TO THEIR ASSIGNED POSITION.

SMOTHER THE FIRE AND PROTECT THE PEOPLE!

RAAH yAy!

...THE ONIWABANSHŪ ARE POPULAR HERE.

HRAAH

HARD TO BELIEVE THEY'RE NINJA...

BM BMBM BMBM

RAAH

WOO-HOO!

GO FOR IT.

144

THERE'S NO NEED FOR SUCH IMPATIENCE.

A LITTLE DELAY, YES.

THEY'RE UP AGAINST 5,000 POLICE. A LITTLE DELAY SHOULD BE NATURAL.

IT'S NOT LIKE ANYONE'S GOING TO FIND US HERE.

...YOU'RE GOING *SOFT* ON ME?

OHH...

SHISHIO-SAMA! DON'T TELL ME...

HIC

HIC

SKWEEZ

WHY WOULD I FEEL NOSTALGIA FOR THIS ROTTEN AGE?

WE'RE SETTING SAIL TO MY GLORY.

YOU'VE HAD TOO MUCH, YUMI.

EVEN IF IT *IS* PART OF YOUR PLAN, TO WATCH MEMORIES BURNING MUST BE HEART-BREAKING, MM?

HIC

SO YOU WANT TO WATCH THE END OF IT.

HIC

...MY FIGHT WITH THAT MAN.

I DO FEEL SOME REGRET AT PUTTING OFF...

...FIREWORKS TO CELEBRATE OUR DECLARATION OF WAR.

THE FLAMES THAT I'M WAITING FOR ARE FIREWORKS...

AND YET, EVEN SO...

DO YOU SEE FLAMES?!

HŌJI-SAMA!

?!

148

HAVE YOU COME TO SEE ME OFF...

...HIMURA BATTŌSAI?!

HEH.

YOUR CLEVERNESS SHALL BE REWARDED...

...HIMURA BATTŌSAI, AND...

...SAITŌ HAJIME, AND...

?

...

Act 101—The Great Kyoto Fire (Part II)

...AT LEAST... I *THINK* HE...

WHO, HIM? JUST A FRIEND OF HIMURA'S.

EH?

SHP

THERE'S ONE I DON'T KNOW.

HMM...

...BUT ONE FAR WEAKER THAN THE OTHER TWO.

SAGARA SANOSUKE. A STREET FIGHTER WELL-KNOWN IN TOKYO...

IN OTHER WORDS...

...A TAGALONG.

STILL...THE BIG SURPRISE IS YET TO COME!

IDIOT.

THE ENEMY'S SURPRISED BY OUR LINEUP.

HEH

AH-CHOO!

154

SO...

WHAT DO WE DO, SHISHIO-SAMA?

SETTLE THE SCORE FROM SHINGETSU VILLAGE?

HSSH

HSSH

HŌJI, GET EVERYONE INSIDE.

AND PREPARE TO GET RID OF THE OUTER LAYER.

OF COURSE, I CAN'T LOOK AS THOUGH I'M RUNNING AWAY.

!

I'D LOVE TO...BUT WE CAN'T WASTE THE TIME HERE.

...AND, ONCE THEY'VE SEEN THE FUTILITY, *THEN* WE'LL LEAVE.

WE'LL SHOW THEM WHAT THEY'RE UP AGAINST...

FWOOO

GLINT

SO, WHAT NOW?

HSSSH

HSSSH

HSSSH

WE GET NEAR THE SHIP, UNDERWATER.

THEN, THE BOTTOM OF THE HULL...

...HOLD ON.

I HAVE SOMETHING BETTER THAN A SWORD.

RUSTLE

IT'S A LITTLE GRENADE KATSU GAVE ME BEFORE I LEFT TOKYO.

IT'S A NEW DESIGN, DOESN'T NEED ANY IGNITION. SO...

HEH

IF YOU DON'T KNOW, YOU'RE AN EVEN BIGGER IDIOT.

YOU'RE STARTING TO WORRY ME, HERE.

AGAIN WITH THE INSULTS! WHAT'S SO IDIOTIC ABOUT...?

NOW, NOW...

RRG RRG RRG

YOU IDIOT.

NEW DESIGN OR NOT, IT'LL NEVER GO OFF.

SANO...EVEN WITHOUT IGNITION, ONCE IT'S UNDERWATER, THE GUNPOWDER WILL BE WET.

KRAK

!

SO... IDIOT...

...YOU JUST COOL YOUR HEELS HERE TILL THE POLICE ARRIVE.

158

YES, SIR.

LET'S GIVE THEM AN EVEN *BIGGER* SURPRISE.

HŌJI. PREPARE THE ARMSTRONG CANNON.

...

HEH...

"METAL SLASH"? NOT UNDER-WATER.

BATTŌSAI, CAN YOU PERFORM "ZANTETSU"?

AN IRONCLAD. IF AN INDIVIDUAL CAN OBTAIN SUCH A THING...

...THE MEIJI GOVERNMENT IS DOOMED EITHER WAY.

...IN PLANS.

CHANGE...

WAIT A MINUTE!

...

ROOOOOM

NO WAY THEY CAN KEEP DODGING GUNS TILL THEN!!

IF I GO HUNTING A BOAT AND SAIL OUT THERE, IT'LL TAKE TOO LONG!

BLAST.

...

FIRST CANNON HIT!

HUH?

NO, THAT'S ENOUGH OF THE ARMSTRONG.

SHALL WE FIRE ANOTHER, SIR?

...AND MAKE IT QUICK.

PREPARE THE GATLING INSTEAD...

GLINT

Act 102
The Great Kyoto Fire (Part III)

175

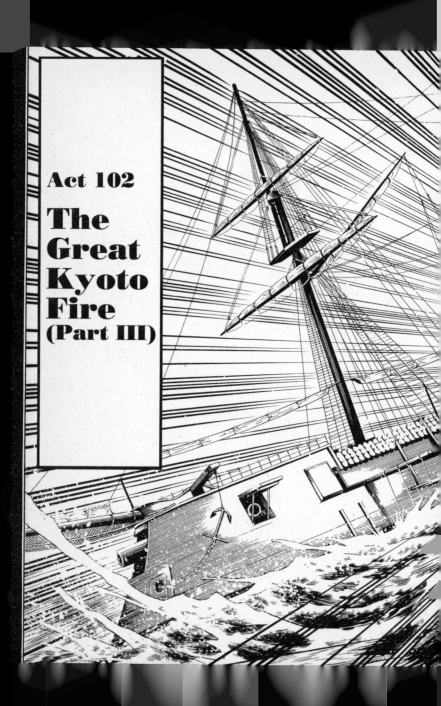

Act 102

The Great Kyoto Fire
(Part III)

178

STILL, IT SURE CAME IN HANDY.

HEH

...CURSE THAT KATSU.

HE HAD ME CARRYING A THING *THAT* DANGEROUS ...?

SOME "SELF-DEFENSE." PFUI.

HAFF

HAFF

JUST YOU WAIT, SHISHIO MAKOTO! I CAN'T *WAIT* TO SEE YOUR EXPRESSION.

FSHH

ALL RIGHTY, THEN!

BLOOSH

SECTORS, REPORT YOUR DAMAGE!!

WE'VE GOT TO REGROUP!

...FEH!

GNG

179

HŌJI-SAMA?!

HŌJI-SAMA, PLEASE ORDER THE EVACUATION!

WOOOOOOH

BAM

IT'S NOT JUST HIM.

!

IT WAS *THAT MAN'S* ARRIVAL THAT UNDID US.

CURSE HIM...

CURSE HIM!

WING WING WING

ALL THAT EFFORT, PUT INTO *RENGOKU...* ALL THOSE WEAPONS, PERSONALLY CHOSEN...

I *REFUSE* TO LOSE TO AN IGNORANT THUG LIKE THAT!

IN OTHER WORDS, OUR LAIR.

THE PLACE MUST BE THE SHRINE OF SIX GATES, LOCATED MIDWAY UP MT. HIEI, ON THE NORTHEAST SIDE.

FINE... ONLY...

ONLY?

WE WILL MEET YOU...THE JUPPONGATANA AND I ALONE!

THERE, WE WILL HAVE NO INTERRUPTIONS.

THERE'S STILL TIME BEFORE THE SHIP SINKS.

NOT TO BE DIFFICULT...

...BUT WOULDN'T TWO-ON-TWO BE QUICKER?

...TEN AGAINST THREE, THEN.

WHY ARE YOU...?

!

THAT'S DETAIL ENOUGH.

A SIX-GATED SHRINE ON HIEI MOUNTAIN.

...

PLEASE, HURRY!

SHISHIO-SAMA, WE'RE READY TO EVACUATE!

186

MUST YOU BE SO HARSH?

COME BACK HERE!

HEY, YOU!

SKWEE

IDIOT.

ARGH!

SHISHIO IS...

SANO'S MORE DEPENDABLE THAN YOU THINK.

GET BACK HERE! NOW!!

WE WOULD NEVER HAVE BEEN ABLE TO SINK *RENGOKU* WITHOUT HIM.

...IT DOESN'T CHANGE THE FACT THAT HE'S AN IDIOT.

BUT EVEN SO...

I KNOW THAT MUCH WITHOUT BEING TOLD.

TP

IT SEEMS THEY'RE FINE OVER THERE.

SURELY, THERE'S BEEN DEATH...

TRUE, BUT AT LEAST WE STOPPED THE GREAT FIRE.

...IS A VICTORY FOR US.

THE FIRST BATTLE...

To Be Continued in Volume 13: A Beautiful Night

GLOSSARY of the RESTORATION

A brief guide to select Japanese terms used in **Rurouni Kenshin**. *Note that, both here and within the story itself, all names are Japanese style—i.e., last or "family" name first, with personal or "given" name following. This is both because* **Kenshin** *is a "period" story, as well as to decrease confusion—if we were to take the example of Kenshin's* sakabatô *and "reverse" the format of the historically established assassin-name "Hitokiri Battôsai," for example, it would make little sense to then call him "Battôsai Himura."*

Ishin Shishi
Loyalist or pro-Imperialist **patriots** who fought to restore the Emperor to his ancient seat of power

Juppongatana
Written with the characters for "ten" and "swords," Shishio's **Juppongatana** are literally that—the ten "swords" or generals he plans to use in his overthrow of Japan

Kamiya Kasshin-ryû
Sword-arts or **kenjutsu** school established by Kaoru's father, who rejected the ethics of **Satsujin-ken** for **Katsujin-ken**

katana
Traditional Japanese longsword (curved, single-edge, worn cutting-edge up) of the samurai. Used primarily for slashing; can be wielded either one- or two-handed.

Katsujin-ken
"Swords that give life"; the sword-arts style developed over ten years by Kaoru's father and founding principle of **Kamiya Kasshin-ryû**

Kawakami Gensai
Real-life, historical inspiration for the character of **Himura Kenshin**

kenjutsu
The art of fencing; sword arts; kendô

Bakumatsu
Final, chaotic days of the Tokugawa regime

-chan
Honorific. Can be used either as a diminutive (e.g., with a small child— "Little Hanako or Kentarô"), or with those who are grown, to indicate affection ("My dear...")

dojo
Martial-arts training hall

-dono
Honorific. Even more respectful than **-san**; the effect in modern-day Japanese conversation would be along the lines of "Milord So-and-So." As used by Kenshin, it indicates both respect and humility.

Edo
Capital city of the **Tokugawa Bakufu**; renamed **Tokyo** ("Eastern Capital") after the Meiji Restoration

Himura Kenshin
Kenshin's "real" name, revealed to Kaoru only at her urging

Hiten Mitsurugi-ryû
Kenshin's sword technique, used more for defense than offense. An "ancient style that pits one against many," it requires exceptional speed and agility to master.

hitokiri
An assassin. Famous swordsmen of the period were sometimes thus known to adopt "professional" names—**Kawakami Gensai**, for example, was also known as "Hitokiri Gensai."

-sama
> Honorific. The respectful equivalent of **-san**, **-sama** is used primarily in addressing persons of much higher rank than one's self...or, in a romantic sense, in addressing those upon whom one is crushing, wicked hard.

-san
> Honorific. Carries the meaning of "Mr.," "Ms.," "Miss," etc., but used more extensively in Japanese than its English equivalent (note that even an enemy may be addressed as "-**san**").

Satsujin-ken
> "Swords that give death"; a style of swordsmanship rejected by Kaoru's father

Shinsengumi
> "True to the old ways and risking their lives to preserve the old **shôgu-nate** system," the popular view of the Shinsengumi ("newly elected group") was that of swordsmen as charismatic as they were skilled. Of note: Thanks to the popularity of the NHK drama of the same name, several historical sites in Japan are reportedly enjoying record attendance levels of late.

shôgun
> Feudal military ruler of Japan

shôgunate
> See **Tokugawa Bakufu**

Tokugawa Bakufu
> Military feudal government which dominated Japan from 1603 to 1867

Tokyo
> The renaming of "**Edo**" to "**Tokyo**" is a marker of the start of the **Meiji Restoration**

Wolves of Mibu
> Nickname for the **Shinsengumi**, so called because of the town (Mibu) where they were first stationed

yatsuhashi
> A traditional Japanese sweet and a Kyoto speciality

-kun
> Honorific. Used in the modern day among male students, or those who grew up together, but another usage—the one you're more likely to find in *Rurouni Kenshin*—is the "superior-to-inferior" form, intended as a way to emphasize a difference in status or rank, as well as to indicate familiarity or affection.

kunoichi
> Female ninja. In that they are not referred to as simply "*onmitsu*" (ninja), their special name suggests their relative scarcity

loyalists
> Those who supported the return of the Emperor to power; **Ishin Shishi**

Meiji Restoration
> 1853-1868; culminated in the collapse of the **Tokugawa Bakufu** and the restoration of imperial rule. So called after Emperor Meiji, whose chosen name was written with the characters for "culture and enlightenment."

patriots
> Another term for **Ishin Shishi**... and when used by Sano, not a flattering one

rurouni
> Wanderer, vagabond

ryûshôsen
> Sometimes translated as "Soaring-Dragon Flash," the **ryûshôsen** of Kenshin's Hiten Mitsurugi school is one of his special moves, and is also known as "Dragon Flight"

ryûkansen
> Also translatable as "Winding-Dragon Flash," Kenshin's Hiten Mitsurugi school special move **ryûkansen** is given in here as "Dragon-Spiral Strike"

sakabatô
> Reversed-edge sword (the dull edge on the side the sharp should be, and vice versa); carried by Kenshin as a symbol of his resolution never to kill again

The Great Kyoto Fire behind them (and casualties relatively few), Kenshin and the others must weigh their next move carefully. The Kyoto-based spy group Oniwabanshû may be trustworthy, but their leader—Shinomori Aoshi—is not. Elsewhere, the monomaniacal madman, Shishio Makoto, makes plans for what is not only practical to his long-range goals, but for also his own, personal pleasure: a one-on-one, to-the-death battle to the finish....

EYESHIELD 21

GEAR UP FOR THE BEST BONE-CRUSHING SLAPSTICK FOOTBALL MANGA EVER!

EYESHIELD 21

SHONEN JUMP ADVANCED

Story by RIICHIRO INAGAKI
Art by YUSUKE MURATA

EYESHIELD 21

Riichiro Inagaki
Yusuke Murata

Vol. 1 On Sale April 5th!

Save 50% off the newsstand price!

THE WORLD'S MOST POPULAR MANGA

Subscribe today and save 50% OFF the cover price, PLUS enjoy all the benefits of the SHONEN JUMP SUBSCRIBER CLUB, exclusive online content & special prizes. ONLY AVAILABLE to SUBSCRIBERS!

☑ **YES!** Please enter my 1 year subscription (12 issues) to *SHONEN JUMP* at the INCREDIBLY LOW SUBSCRIPTION RATE of $29.95, and sign me up for the Shonen Jump Subscriber Club.

$29⁹⁵

NAME

ADDRESS

CITY   STATE   ZIP

E-MAIL ADDRESS

☐ **MY CHECK IS ENCLOSED**   ☐ **BILL ME LATER**

CREDIT CARD: ☐ **VISA**   ☐ **MASTERCARD**

ACCOUNT #   EXP. DATE

SIGNATURE

CLIP AND MAIL TO ➡

SHONEN JUMP
Subscriptions Service Dept.
P.O. Box 515
Mount Morris, IL 61054-0515

Make checks payable to: **SHONEN JUMP.**
Canada add US $12. No foreign orders. Allow 6-8 weeks for delivery.

P5SJGN   YU-GI-OH! © 1996 by KAZUKI TAKAHASHI / SHUEISHA Inc.

COMPLETE OUR SURVEY AND LET US KNOW WHAT YOU THINK!

☐ Please do NOT send me information about VIZ and SHONEN JUMP products, news and events, special offers, or other information.

☐ Please do NOT send me information from VIZ's trusted business partners.

Name: _____

Address: _____

City:_____ State:_____ Zip:_____

E-mail: _____

☐ Male ☐ Female Date of Birth (mm/dd/yyyy): __ / __ / ____ (Under 13? Parental consent required)

① Do you purchase SHONEN JUMP Magazine?

☐ Yes ☐ No (if no, skip the next two questions)

If **YES**, do you subscribe?

☐ Yes ☐ No

If **NO**, how often do you purchase SHONEN JUMP Magazine?

☐ 1-3 issues a year

☐ 4-6 issues a year

☐ more than 7 issues a year

② Which SHONEN JUMP Graphic Novel did you purchase? (please check one)

☐ Beet the Vandel Buster ☐ Bleach ☐ Dragon Ball

☐ Dragon Ball Z ☐ Hikaru no Go ☐ Knights of the Zodiac

☐ Naruto ☐ One Piece ☐ Rurouni Kenshin

☐ Shaman King ☐ The Prince of Tennis ☐ Ultimate Muscle

☐ Whistle! ☐ Yu-Gi-Oh! ☐ YuYu Hakusho

☐ Other_____

Will you purchase subsequent volumes?

☐ Yes ☐ No

③ How did you learn about this title? (check all that apply)

☐ Favorite title ☐ Advertisement ☐ Article

☐ Gift ☐ Read excerpt in SHONEN JUMP Magazine

☐ Recommendation ☐ Special offer ☐ Through TV animation

☐ Website ☐ Other_____

...JUMP Magazine have you purchased the

c l

☐ ...Yes

W9-CUG-964

If YES, wh... ...check all that apply)

☐ Dragon ... Z   ☐ ...o Go   ☐ Naruto   ☐ One Piece

☐ Shaman King   ☐ ...i-G...   ☐ YuYu Hakusho

...ES wha... ...or ...ising? (please pick up to 3)

☐ ...rite titl...   ☐ ...orite creator/artist   ☐ I want to read it in one go

☐ I want to r... ...ag...in   ☐ There are extras that aren't in the magazine

☐ ...qua... pri... ...han the magazine   ☐ Recommendation

☐ Sp...ific... ...r

If NO, why ...ould y... ...e ?

☐ ...just reading ...magazine   ☐ It's not worth buying the graphic novel

☐ ...e manga r... b...k and white unlike the magazine

☐ ...els that I prefer   ☐ There are too many to collect for each title

☐ ... ...   ☐ Other _____

...the ...OT ...er... in the Magazine, which ones have you purchased?
...eck all tha... ...ly)

☐ Beet the Vandel Buster   ☐ Bleach   ☐ Dragon Ball

☐ Knights of the Zodiac   ☐ The Prince of Tennis   ☐ Rurouni Kenshin

☐ Whistle!   ☐ Other _____   ☐ None

If you did purchase any of the above, what were your reasons for purchase?

☐ A favorite title   ☐ A favorite creator/artist

☐ Read a preview in SHONEN JUMP Magazine and wanted to read the rest of the story

☐ Recommendation   ☐ Other

Will you purchase subsequent volumes?

☐ Yes   ☐ No

6 What race/ethnicity do you consider yourself? (please check one)

☐ Asian/Pacific Islander   ☐ Black/African American   ☐ Hispanic/Latino

☐ Native American/Alaskan Native   ☐ White/Caucasian   ☐ Other

THANK YOU! Please send the completed form to: VIZ Survey
42 Catharine St.
Poughkeepsie, NY 12601